Shapes
for Lunch
Figuras para el almuerzo

by Deborah Schecter

ISBN: 978-1-338-70291-0
Illustrated by Anne Kennedy
Copyright © 2020 by Deborah Schecter. All rights reserved.
Published by Scholastic Inc., 557 Broadway, New York, NY 10012

10 9 8 7 6   68   23 24 25 26/0

Printed in Jiaxing, China. First printing, June 2020.

I like to eat a square.

Me gusta comer cuadrados.

I like to eat a triangle.

Me gusta comer triángulos.

I like to eat an oval.

Me gusta comer óvalos.

I like to eat a rectangle.

Me gusta comer rectángulos.

I like to eat a circle.

Me gusta comer círculos.

I like to eat a half-circle.

Me gusta comer semicírculos.

Shapes are fun for lunch!

¡Comer figuras
es muy divertido!